#1 AUTUMN/WINTER 2015

CHART HITS

WISE PUBLICATIONS
PART OF THE MUSIC SALES GROUP
LONDON / NEW YORK / PARIS / SYDNEY / COPENHAGEN / BERLIN / MADRID / HONG KONG / TOKYO

ALSO AVAILABLE IN THE REALLY EASY PIANO SERIES...

ABBA
25 GREAT HITS. ORDER NO. AM980430

CHILDREN'S FAVOURITES
20 POPULAR HITS. ORDER NO. AM998745

CHRISTMAS
24 FESTIVE CHART HITS. ORDER NO. AM980496

CLASSICAL FAVOURITES
24 WELL-KNOWN FAVOURITES. ORDER NO. AM993366

COLDPLAY
20 SONGS FROM COLDPLAY. ORDER NO. AM1009547

ELTON JOHN
24 CLASSIC SONGS. ORDER NO. AM987844

FRANK SINATRA
21 CLASSIC SONGS. ORDER NO. AM987833

GREAT FILM SONGS
22 BIG FILM HITS. ORDER NO. AM993344

GREAT SHOWSTOPPERS
20 POPULAR STAGE SONGS. ORDER NO. AM993355

JAZZ GREATS
22 JAZZ FAVOURITES. ORDER NO. AM1000857

LOVE SONGS
22 CLASSIC LOVE SONGS. ORDER NO. AM989582

MICHAEL JACKSON
19 CLASSIC HITS. ORDER NO. AM1000604

MORE 21ST CENTURY HITS
21 POPULAR HITS. ORDER NO. AM996534

MOZART
22 CLASSICAL FAVOURITES. ORDER NO. AM1000648

NEW CHART HITS
19 BIG CHART HITS. ORDER NO. AM996523

NO. 1 HITS
22 POPULAR CLASSICS. ORDER NO. AM993388

POP HITS
22 GREAT SONGS. ORDER NO. AM980408

SHOWSTOPPERS
24 STAGE HITS. ORDER NO. AM982784

TV HITS
25 POPULAR HITS. ORDER NO. AM985435

60S HITS
25 CLASSIC HITS. ORDER NO. AM985402

70S HITS
25 CLASSIC SONGS. ORDER NO. AM985413

80S HITS
25 POPULAR HITS. ORDER NO. AM985424

90S HITS
24 POPULAR HITS. ORDER NO. AM987811

50 FABULOUS SONGS
FROM POP SONGS TO CLASSICAL THEMES. ORDER NO. AM999449

50 GREAT SONGS
FROM POP SONGS TO CLASSICAL THEMES. ORDER NO. AM995643

50 HIT SONGS
FROM POP HITS TO JAZZ CLASSICS. ORDER NO. AM1000615

PIANO TUTOR
FROM FIRST STEPS TO PLAYING IN A WIDE
RANGE OF STYLES — FAST!. ORDER NO. AM996303

ALL TITLES CONTAIN BACKGROUND NOTES FOR EACH SONG PLUS
PLAYING TIPS AND HINTS.

PUBLISHED BY
WISE PUBLICATIONS
14-15 BERNERS STREET, LONDON, W1T 3LJ, UK.

EXCLUSIVE DISTRIBUTORS:
MUSIC SALES LIMITED
DISTRIBUTION CENTRE, NEWMARKET ROAD, BURY ST EDMUNDS,
SUFFOLK, IP33 3YB, UK.
MUSIC SALES PTY LIMITED
LEVEL 4, 30-32 CARRINGTON STREET,
SYDNEY, NSW 2000 AUSTRALIA.

ORDER NO. AM1011054
ISBN 978-1-78558-061-1
THIS BOOK © COPYRIGHT 2015 BY WISE PUBLICATIONS,
A DIVISION OF MUSIC SALES LIMITED.

ARRANGED BY FIONA BOLTON.
EDITED BY JENNI NOREY.
PRINTED IN THE EU.

YOUR GUARANTEE OF QUALITY
AS PUBLISHERS, WE STRIVE TO PRODUCE EVERY BOOK TO THE HIGHEST
COMMERCIAL STANDARDS. THE MUSIC HAS BEEN FRESHLY ENGRAVED AND
THE BOOK HAS BEEN CAREFULLY DESIGNED TO MINIMISE AWKWARD PAGE
TURNS AND TO MAKE PLAYING FROM IT A REAL PLEASURE.
PARTICULAR CARE HAS BEEN GIVEN TO SPECIFYING ACID-FREE, NEUTRAL-
SIZED PAPER MADE FROM PULPS WHICH HAVE NOT BEEN ELEMENTAL
CHLORINE BLEACHED. THIS PULP IS FROM FARMED SUSTAINABLE FORESTS
AND WAS PRODUCED WITH SPECIAL REGARD FOR THE ENVIRONMENT.
THROUGHOUT, THE PRINTING AND BINDING HAVE BEEN PLANNED TO
ENSURE A STURDY, ATTRACTIVE PUBLICATION WHICH SHOULD GIVE YEARS
OF ENJOYMENT. IF YOUR COPY FAILS TO MEET OUR HIGH STANDARDS,
PLEASE INFORM US AND WE WILL GLADLY REPLACE IT.

WWW.MUSICSALES.COM

CHART HITS

Blank Space

Words & Music by Max Martin, Taylor Swift
& Shellback

With its clever lyrics, minimalist electropop beat and a wonderfully catchy melody, this has become one of Taylor Swift's best-loved songs and an instant pop classic. The second single from her wildly successful fifth album *1989*, Taylor became the first woman ever to have two consecutive No. 1 spots on the Billboard Hot 100.

Hints & Tips: Practise the right-hand rhythm in bars 3 & 5 carefully, tapping or counting the quaver beats out loud to help with the timing.

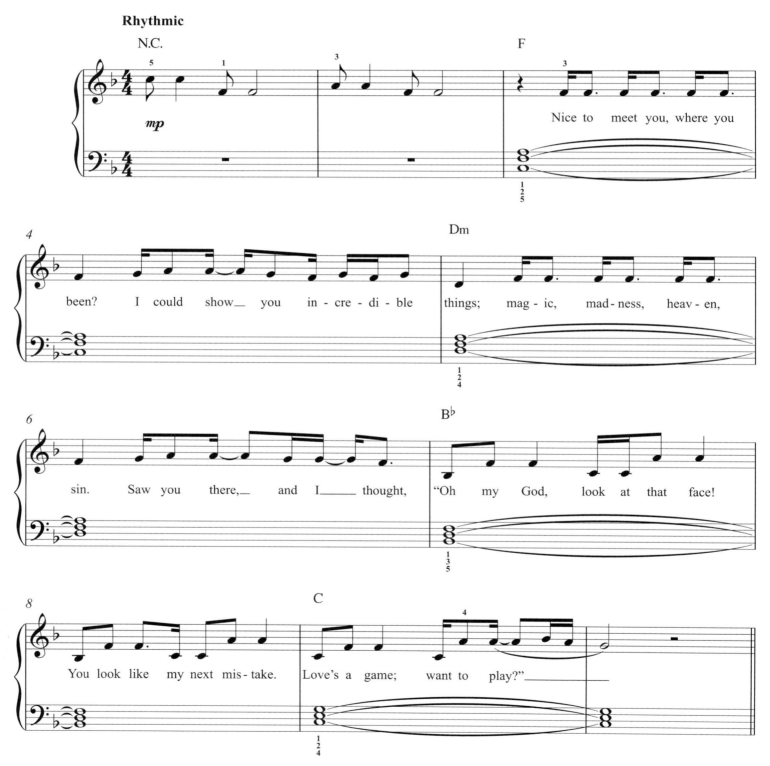

Bills

**Words & Music by Jacob Hindlin, Eric Frederic,
Rickard Goransson & Gamal Lewis**

Rocketing from relative unknown to No. 2 on the UK singles chart, Gamal 'LunchMoney' Lewis composed this unusually catchy hit in just 30 minutes. The song's co-writer Ricky Reed (aka Eric Frederic) stated that he wanted to do a modern twist on the gospel rag, combining an ingenious piano riff with electronic drums and production.

Hints & Tips: In bar 4 you will need to leap down to the C with your left thumb; make sure you're ready so you hit the right note. The rhythms from bar 9 are quite fast. To avoid them blurring together, play slightly detached (*staccato*).

Heartbeat Song

Words & Music by Kara Dioguardi, Kelly Clarkson, Audra Butts & Jason Evigan

Opening Kelly Clarkson's 2015 album *Piece By Piece*, 'Heartbeat Song' is a return to her upbeat pop brilliance, after her last single release in 2013. During this period away from music, Clarkson got married and had her first child. The optimistic tone of the lyrics works perfectly together with the uptempo electropop rhythm that is based on the actual heartbeat of her child.

Hints & Tips: There are lots of syncopated rhythms in the right hand, but the steady quavers and crotchets in the left hand should give you a reference for where the main beats of the bar fall.

Fireproof

Words & Music by John Ryan, Jamie Scott,
Julian Bunetta, Liam Payne & Louis Tomlinson

When 1D's album *Four* was announced, this track was made available as a free download for a limited 24 hour period. In just that day, it was downloaded over one million times, setting a new record for the most downloaded free track ever. The success of the song is testament to the brilliant vocal performances and the catchiness of the melody, co-written by Louis and Liam with Jamie Scott, who says this is one of his favourite tunes on the album.

Hints & Tips: Play through hands separately until you're confident with the fingering for both before putting them together. Remember to play B♭s throughout.

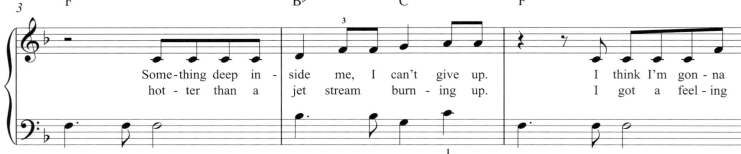

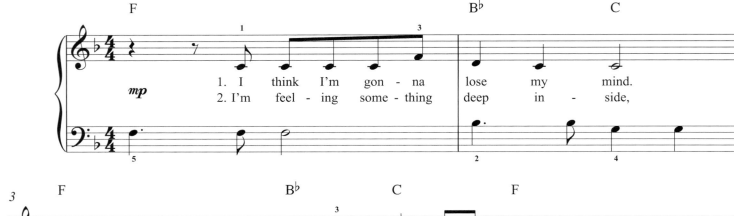

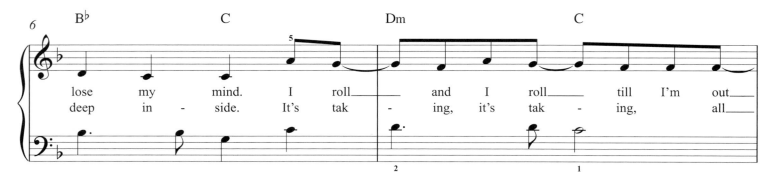

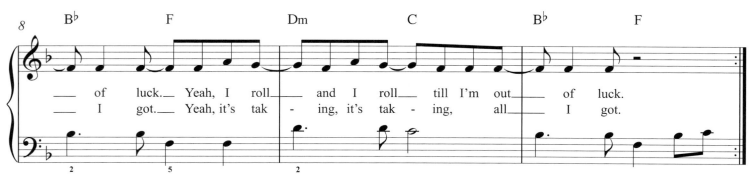

Flashlight

**Words & Music by Jason Moore, Sia Furler,
Sam Smith, Christian Guzman & Mario Mejia**

'Flashlight' is a downtempo ballad that was composed for the soundtrack of *Pitch Perfect 2* collaboratively by pop powerhouses Sia, Sam Smith, Christian Guzman and Jason Moore. Jessie J's performance is strong and note-perfect, unleashing the passionate vocals for which she has come to be known. The song works perfectly as the emotional climax of the movie, while the music video sees Jessie J visiting the film's fictional university to perform.

Hints & Tips: Keep the left-hand quavers steady and even. When the right hand plays in thirds, as in bar 9, make sure the notes sound exactly together.

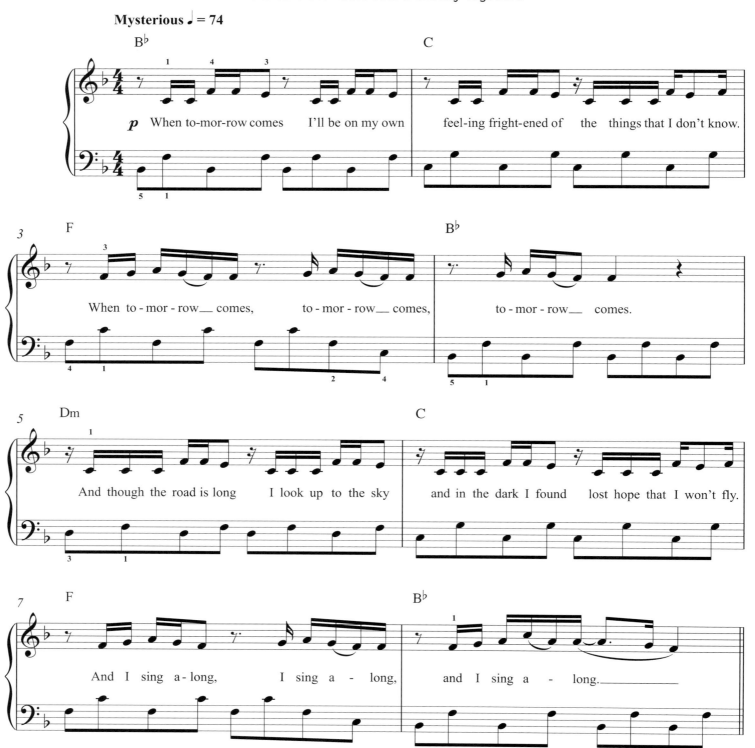

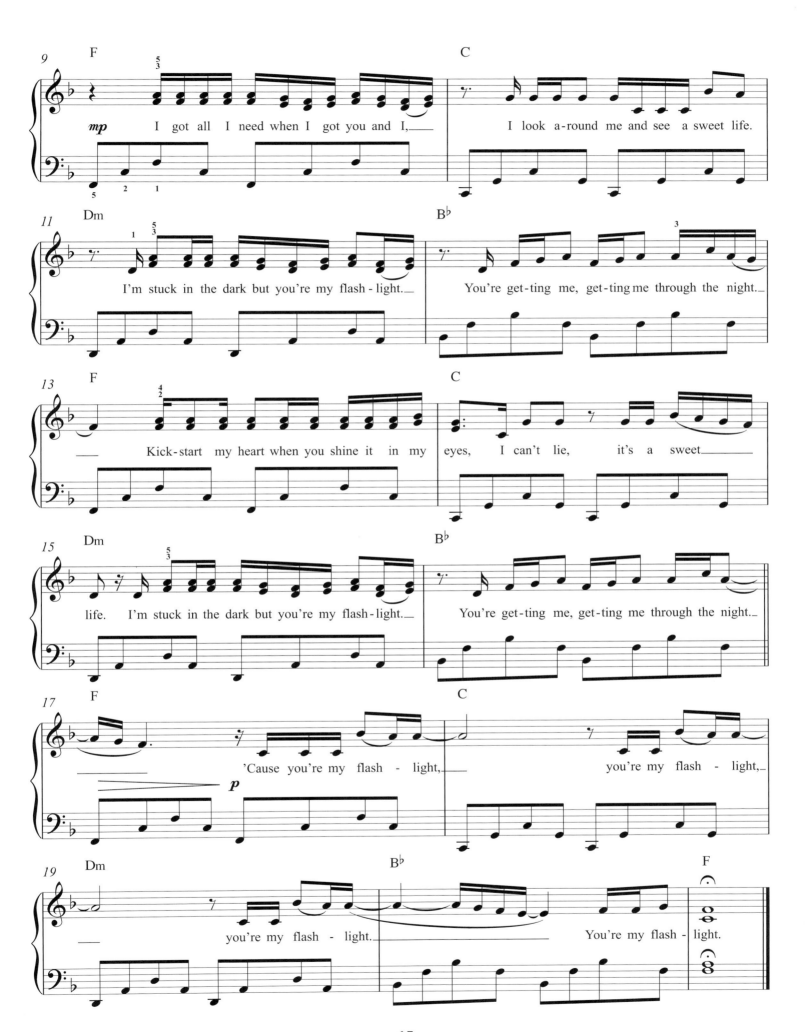

FourFive Seconds

Words & Music by Rihanna, Paul McCartney
& Kanye West

'FourFive Seconds' is a song by pop superstar Rihanna, hip hop giant Kanye West and Beatles legend Paul McCartney. With such a super-group of singing and song-writing talent, the success of the song with critics and music lovers was no surprise. What was unusual was the stripped-down minimalism and the almost folk-country feeling of just vocals, guitar and organ.

Hints & Tips: Make sure you keep the bottommost notes in the left hand held down with the fifth finger, while keeping the crotchets moving. Sometimes it's quite a stretch so check your fingers are in the best position.

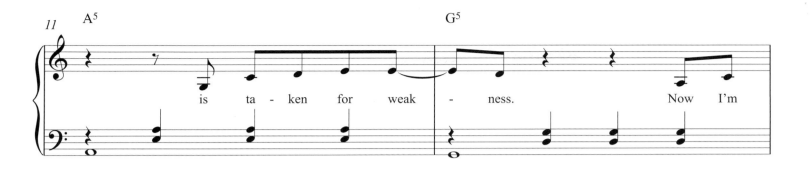

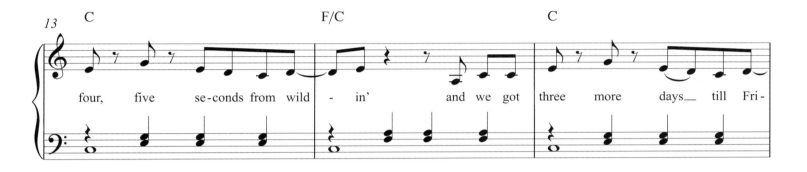

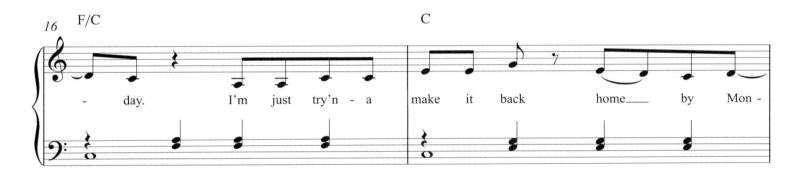

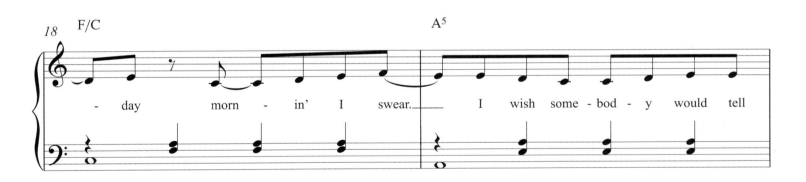

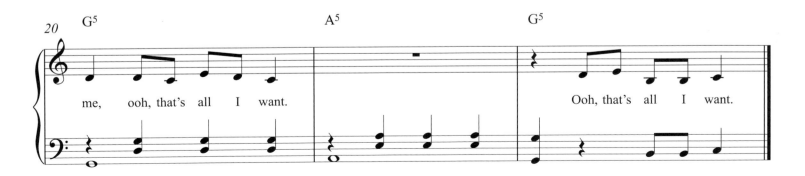

Hold My Hand

Words & Music by Ina Wroldsen, Jack Patterson,
Jess Glynne & Janee Bennett

After topping the charts as the vocal talent behind Clean Bandit's biggest song, 'Rather Be', Jess Glynne has taken the top spot on her own with this anthem about someone being there for you in a tough time. Written with Jack Patterson from Clean Bandit and Glynne's friend Janee Bennett, Jess shows off her wide vocal range in a song that she says happened to come out sounding a little like Dolly Parton's hit '9 to 5'.

Hints & Tips: This is a fun song, so keep it light and bouncy. Make the most of the different dynamic contrasts, starting off fairly quiet (*mp*) at the start and ending up loud (*f*) at the end.

Put your arms__ a-round me, tell__ me

ev -'ry-thing's__ O - K.

Break my__ bones but__ you won't__ see me__ fall,_____ whoa.__

cresc. poco a poco

_____ The ris - ing__ tide will__ rise a - gainst them__

all,_____ whoa._____ Darl - ing, hold my hand._____

mf

19

20

I Really Like You

Words & Music by Peter Svensson, Carly Rae Jepsen
& Jacob Hindlin

Reportedly, when making plans for her third album *Emotion*, Carly Rae Jepsen's manager told her she couldn't release anything unless it was on the level of her biggest hit 'Call Me Maybe'. She then released this danceable pop number 'I Really Like You', whose chorus ensures it'll go down in pop history. The lyrics are about being in a relationship where it's just too soon to say "I love you".

Hints & Tips: Check the right-hand fingering all the way through. Practise any tricky sections, such as the start of the chorus in bar 17, on their own.

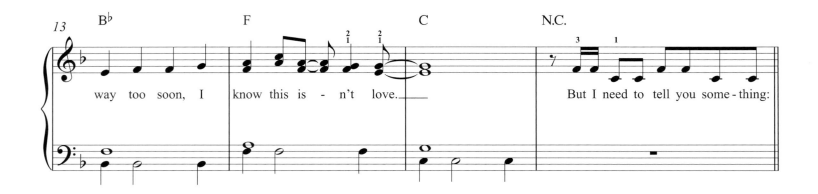

Oh, _____ did I say too much? I'm so in

my head when we're out - ta touch, out - ta touch!

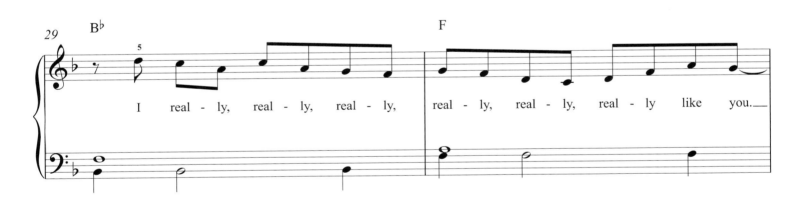

I real - ly, real - ly, real - ly, real - ly, real - ly, real - ly like you. _

_ And I want you, do you want me, do you want me too?

King

**Words & Music by Andrew Smith, Oliver Thornton,
Michael Goldsworthy, Resul Turkmen & Mark Ralph**

The electropop band Years & Years won the prestigious BBC Sound of 2015 poll before releasing 'King', the fourth single from their debut album, *Communion*. Both single and album reached No. 1 in the UK Charts, making Years & Years a mainstay on festival stages throughout the summer. Singer Olly Alexander says that the hugely danceable song is about feeling like a king while in a relationship, yet knowing it has to end.

Hints & Tips: Practise this slowly at first then build up the speed when you're comfortable with playing hands together; this is quite an upbeat song and shouldn't drag.

Lay Me Down

Words & Music by James Napier, Sam Smith
& Elvin Smith

'Lay Me Down' was the debut single from the debut album of British singing sensation Sam Smith. Smith chose to re-release the single after the success of his album, and also recorded a version with John Legend for 2015's Red Nose Day. A beautiful piano-based ballad about unrequited love, the song shows off the young singer's songwriting abilities as well as his stunning vocal range, moving through registers hitting every note perfectly.

Hints & Tips: There are some tricky chords in the left hand. Play them all through slowly at first, one after the other, taking time to make sure you've got your fingers in the right place before pressing the keys.

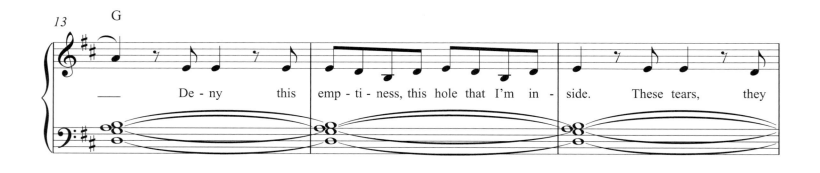

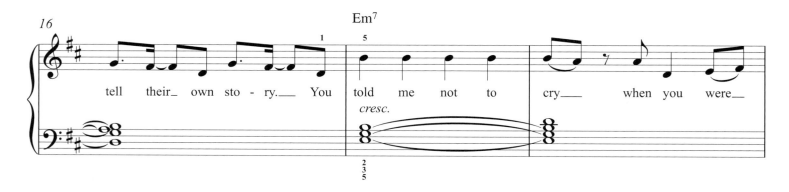

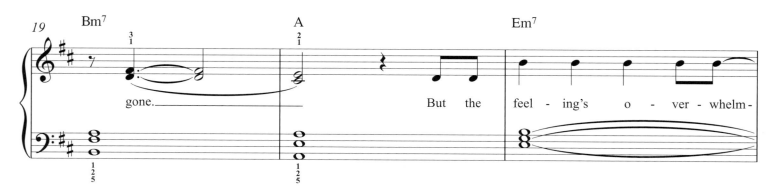

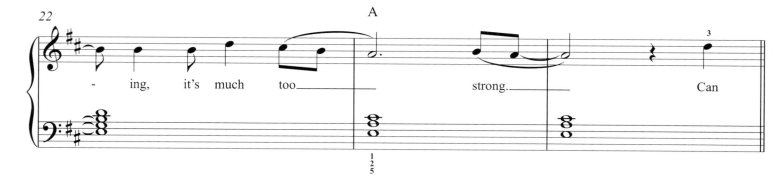

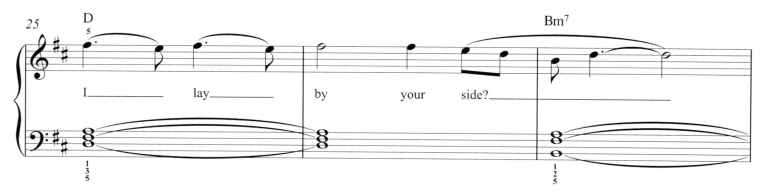

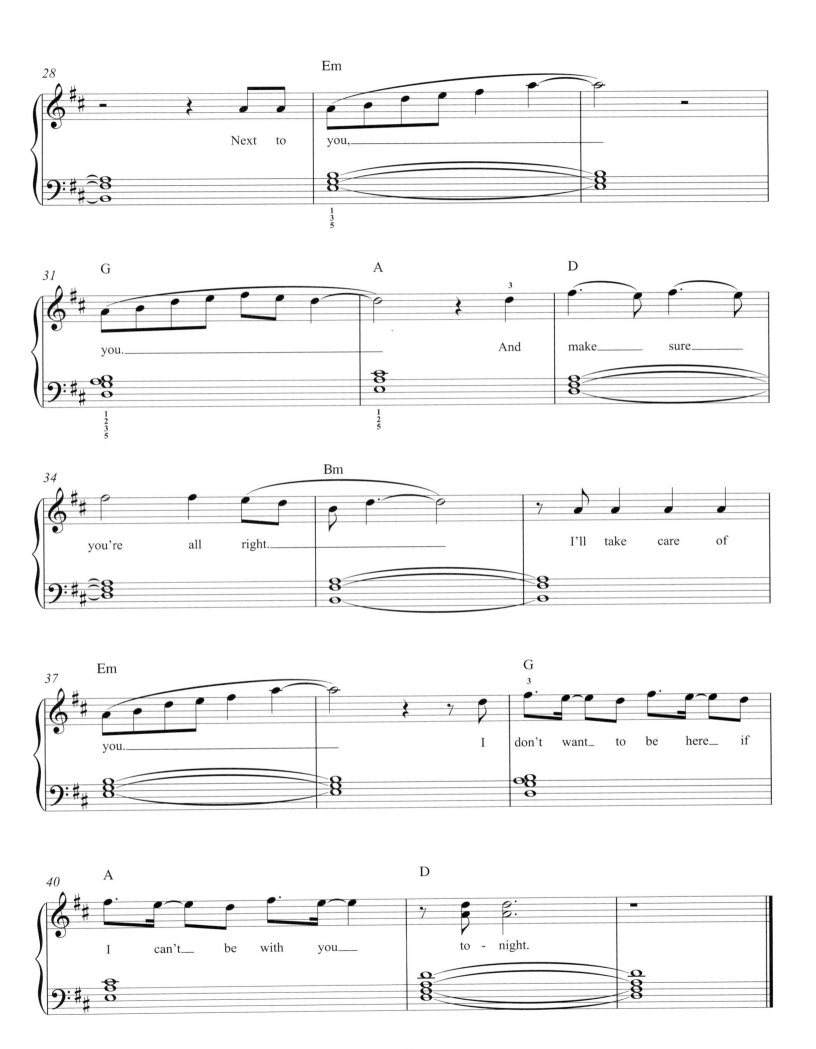

The Nights

Words & Music by Tim Bergling, John Feldmann, Ash Pournouri,
Nicholas Furlong, Gabriel Benjamin Budin-Smithers & Jordan Suecof

Avicii's unique style of blending the uplifting elements of traditional dance music with folk and country instruments is nowhere more apparent than in 'The Nights', a collaboration with singer Nicholas 'RAS' Furlong. Furlong wrote the song as an ode to his father, who told him to live an eventful life that he would remember.

Hints & Tips: While the rhythms and notes of the instrumental section (from bar 25) aren't that difficult, you may want to play this through a few times; the repetitiveness can make your fingers trip up!

Photograph

Words & Music by Ed Sheeran & John McDaid

Combining guitar strumming, a simple piano riff and lyrics about love, loss and memories, this is a perfect example of Ed Sheeran's wonderfully emotional songwriting. While Sheeran was on tour with Snow Patrol, he and their guitarist Johnny McDaid wrote this song together in a hotel room. Sheeran was reportedly playing with Lego while McDaid worked on his laptop and they both grew this song from the initial piano melody!

Hints & Tips: The left-hand rhythm might look challenging, but it's pretty much the same all the way through, so once you've got the hang of how it goes it should be easy!

Hold Back The River

Words & Music by Iain Archer & James Bay

Opening the second single from James Bay's album is a quiet guitar riff that opens up a heartfelt verse before giving way to the anthemic chorus. According to Bay, the song is about the feeling of being unable to see friends and family during a busy touring and recording schedule. After winning the Critics' Choice award at the Brits 2015 and seeing his album hit No. 1 in the UK Chart, his diary was so demanding that he welcomed the opportunity to finally see his friends and family.

Hints & Tips: Watch out at the start, as both hands are playing the same rhythm but different notes. Keep it steady and precise.

back the riv - er, let me look in your eyes. Hold back the riv - er so I can stop

for a min-ute and be by your side. Hold back the riv - er, hold back. Hold

back the riv - er, let me look in your eyes. Hold back the riv - er so I can stop

for a min-ute and see where you hide. Hold back the riv - er, hold back.

See You Again

Words & Music by Justin Franks, Cameron Thomaz, Charlie Puth & Andrew Cedar

This heartfelt hip-hop track forms part of the soundtrack to the tearful final few minutes of the film *Furious 7*, which is a tribute to the late actor Paul Walker, who passed away while working on the film. Charlie Puth's emotive singing and subtle piano punctuate Wiz Khalifa's raps about love and loss. The song hit a personal note for many involved as well as fans of the film franchise, with the uplifting track being seen as a very fitting tribute.

Hints & Tips: Notice that the vocal melody line is played by the left hand throughout. Keep the right-hand chords quiet to allow the tune to come through.

Ship To Wreck

Words & Music by Florence Welch & Thomas Hull

After Florence + The Machine's second album, lead singer Florence Welch decided to take a year off to begin working on ideas for the next album. The awesome 'Ship To Wreck' is the second single from this long-awaited album, foregrounding Florence's powerful vocals over acoustic guitar, a driving bassline and upbeat drums. Florence has stated that the song is about her "self-destructive side" and almost didn't make the album's final cut.

Hints & Tips: Keep the quavers in the left hand even and light; don't play them too loud or they'll drown out the tune. From bar 33, however, the left hand has a more prominent part, and so you should bring this out more.

Stronger

Words & Music by Grace Chatto, Jack Patterson,
Oz Moses & George Moore

The classical quartet turned dance group enlisted the help of *Glee* star Alex Newell and Sean Bass, who is the brother of Sharna Bass who sang on Clean Bandit's earlier single 'Extraordinary'. The music video for 'Stronger' featured fifty mobile phones which were used to achieve the unique 'bullet time' effect seen during the band's dance sequence.

Hints & Tips: This song is very percussive and will need playing with confidence to make it sound effective! The right and left hand both have their parts to play and the rhythms need to be precise.

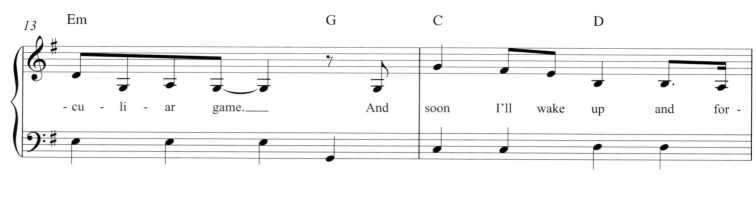

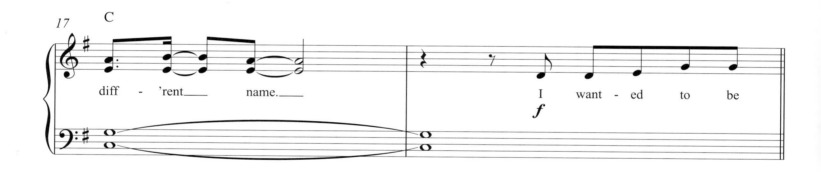

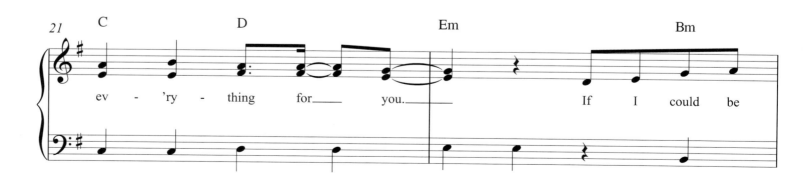

Someone New

**Words & Music by Andrew Hozier-Byrne
& Sallay Garnett**

With a retro, soulful and blues-inspired sound, this atmospheric tune tells the story of the dark side of love. The fifth single from Hozier's critically acclaimed self-titled album, the video for 'Someone New' stars *Game of Thrones* actress Natalie Dormer as a dark and mysterious figure in the crowds, while Hozier performs on stage.

Hints & Tips: The rhythms of the left hand look quite complicated, but the tempo isn't too fast. Take it slow to begin with and clap through any rhythms you're not sure of.

COLLECT THE SERIES...

BIG CHART HITS
19 BIG CHART HITS
FEATURING SONGS SUCH AS
THE A TEAM, JAR OF HEARTS
AND SET FIRE TO THE RAIN.

ORDER NO. AM1004839

SONGS FROM
THE MOVIES
16 GREAT FILM SONGS
INCLUDING: EVERYTHING IS
AWESOME, HAPPY, SKYFALL,
A THOUSAND YEARS.

ORDER NO. AM1009932

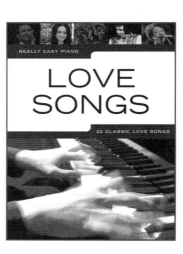

LOVE SONGS
22 POPULAR LOVE SONGS
WITH HITS SUCH AS
AIN'T NO SUNSHINE, CRAZY,
FEVER, HAVE I TOLD YOU
LATELY, LIKE A STAR AND
LOVE ME TENDER.

ORDER NO. AM989582

MORE CLASSICAL
FAVOURITES
21 CLASSICAL FAVOURITES
INCLUDING: AVE MARIA,
IMPROMPTU NO.3,
RONDO ALLA TURCA,
VOCALISE.

ORDER NO. AM1010625

OVER 30 TITLES AVAILABLE...

REALLY EASY PIANO: ABBA
AM980430

REALLY EASY PIANO: ADELE
AM1004036

REALLY EASY PIANO: BALLADS
AM982751

REALLY EASY PIANO: THE BEATLES
NO91080

REALLY EASY PIANO: CHRISTMAS
AM980496

REALLY EASY PIANO: CHRISTMAS CAROLS
AM985446

REALLY EASY PIANO: CHRISTMAS HITS
AM1009745

REALLY EASY PIANO: CLASSICAL
AM980419

REALLY EASY PIANO: CLASSICAL FAVOURITES
AM993366

REALLY EASY PIANO: COLDPLAY
AM1009547

REALLY EASY PIANO: ED SHEERAN
AM1009800

REALLY EASY PIANO: ELTON JOHN
AM987844

REALLY EASY PIANO: FILM SONGS
AM980441

REALLY EASY PIANO: FILM THEMES
AM982762

REALLY EASY PIANO: FRANK SINATRA
AM987833

REALLY EASY PIANO: GERSHWIN
AM997249

REALLY EASY PIANO: JAZZ
AM982773

REALLY EASY PIANO: NEW CHART HITS
AM996523

REALLY EASY PIANO: NEW HITS NOW!
AM1009206

REALLY EASY PIANO: NO.1 HITS
AM993388

REALLY EASY PIANO: ONE DIRECTION
AM1006632

REALLY EASY PIANO: ONE DIRECTION SONGBOOK
AM1010812

REALLY EASY PIANO: ONE DIRECTION VOLUME 2
AM1010482

REALLY EASY PIANO: POP HITS
AM980408

REALLY EASY PIANO: GREAT SHOWSTOPPERS
AM993355

REALLY EASY PIANO: SHOWSTOPPERS
AM982784

REALLY EASY PIANO: TV HITS
AM985435

REALLY EASY PIANO: 70S HITS
AM985413

REALLY EASY PIANO: 80S HITS
AM985424

REALLY EASY PIANO: 90S HITS
AM987811

REALLY EASY PIANO: 21ST CENTURY HITS
AM987822

REALLY EASY PIANO: 101 TOP HITS
AM1008975

...PLUS MANY MORE!